What to doodle? Jr.
ANIMALS!

Note

Here are some doodling challenges for you: draw spots for a baby leopard, show what a tiger's teeth look like, decorate a hermit crab's shell, add a fin to a seahorse, and much more! In this little book, you'll find dozens of pages that just need your finishing touches to be complete. All you need is your imagination—and a pencil—to create pictures of dozens of zoo and aquarium creatures. Let's get started!

What is the buffalo grazing on?

What's missing on the mommy giraffe?

Giraffes have really long necks to reach
the leaves at the top of the tree.
Can you draw this giraffe's
really long neck?

What is the panda eating?

What do a panda's eyes look like?

Where are the crocodile's teeth?
Draw them!

open wide!

What patterns would look nice on these crocodiles?

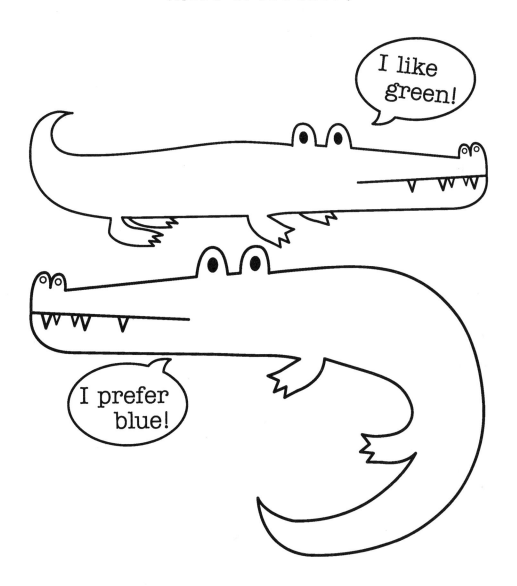

Can you draw an igloo for these penguins?

What does a lion's mouth look like?

Can you draw the lion's mane?

What do the spots look like on this baby leopard?

What is this mommy leopard looking for?

What does a monkey's face look like?

Who is swinging from the tree?

How many horns does a rhino have?

The rhino wants to find a place to cool off from the sun. Can you draw him a pond to get some water?

What do a walrus's teeth look like?

What does the baby walrus need so she can swim?

What patterns do the zebras have?

What do zebras like to eat?

What is the polar bear standing on?

What can the polar bear see
in the water?

Can you draw a hippo's face?

Where does the hippo like to
take a bath?

What is the seal looking at over
the rocks?

What is the seal playing with?

What's at the end of the rattlesnake's tail?

What patterns can you give
these snakes?

The gorilla likes to play in the trees. Can you draw some more?

What is on the ground for him
to eat?

What do the elephants need to take a bath?

Draw it on these pages.

How does the koala hold on to the tree?

What does a koala's nose look like?

What kind of tail does the
Red Panda have?

Draw a friend for the Red Panda.

What are these meerkats looking at?

Who is in the kangaroo's pouch?

What is the kangaroo jumping over?

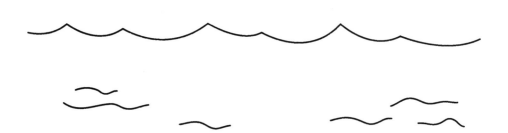

What kind of legs do flamingos have?

Where is the flamingo standing?

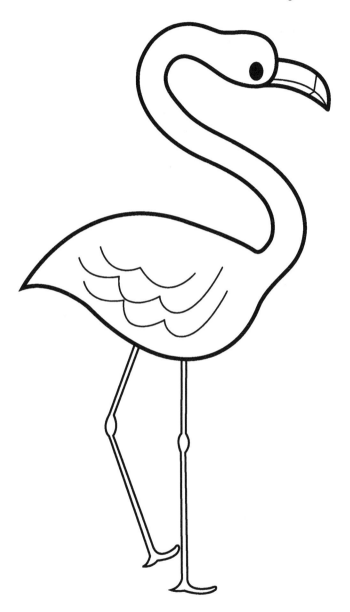

What is the toucan sitting on?

What kind of beak does the
toucan have?

What is missing from the tiger's fur?

What do a tiger's teeth look like?

What kind of eyes does an owl have?

Owls are always up at night.
What is in the sky above the owl?

How many humps does a camel have?

Can you draw some sand
for the camels?

Can you draw a tortoise shell?

What patterns would look good on
these tortoises?

Where will this wolf go to sleep?

What is the wolf dreaming about?

How many legs does a tarantula have?

Can you help design this spider's web?

What kind of tail does this lemur have?

Can you draw a snack for the lemur family?

It's feeding time at the zoo!
Who's hungry?

How many tentacles does an octopus have?

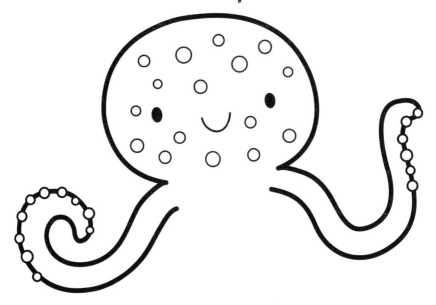

Can you give this octopus
different patterns?

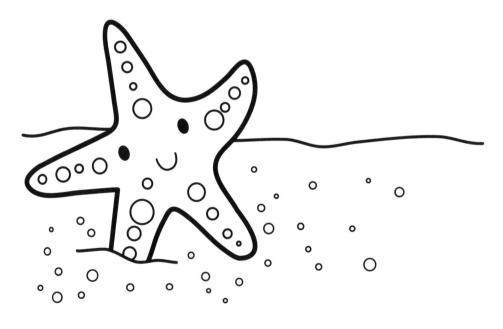

Who is the starfish waving at?

Can you finish drawing these starfish?

Who is the whale swimming with?

Whales breathe through their blowholes.
What happens when he comes up for air?

Sea turtles have patterns on their flippers.
Can you help decorate these flippers?

What is the sea turtle hiding behind?

Who is hiding under the rocks?

Can you draw some fins for these sharks?

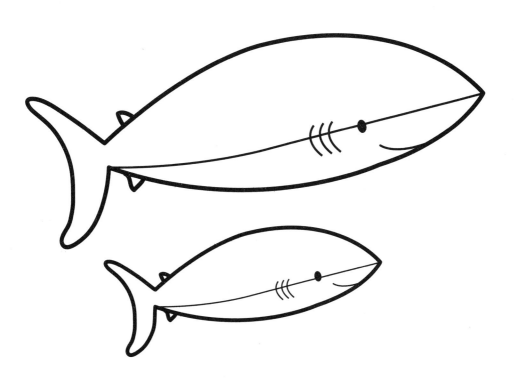

What is the dolphin diving into?

Dolphins like to play.
What are they chasing?

Who's inside the clam shell?

What do you think
the inside of the shell looks like?

Lobsters have two large claws. Can you draw the missing one?

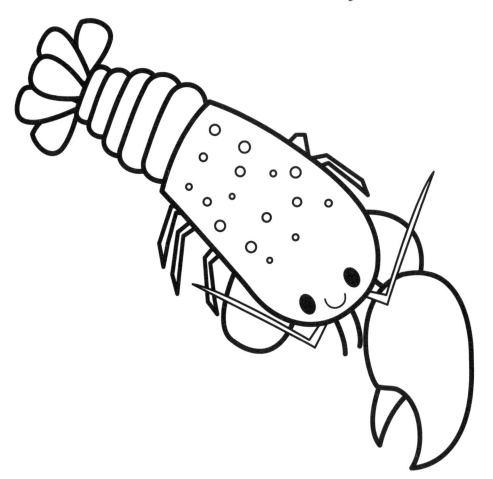

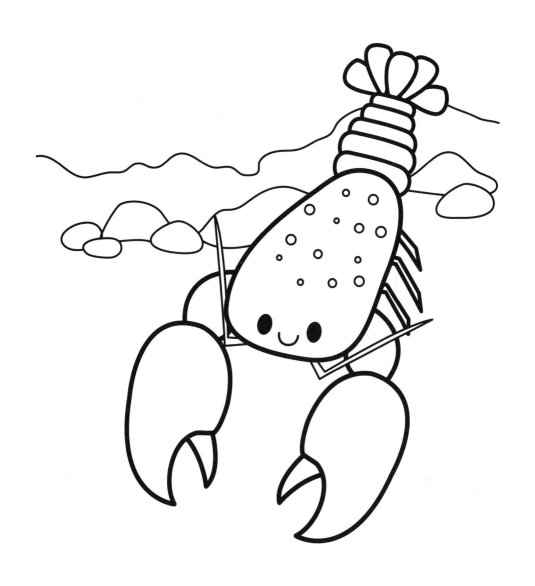

What is the lobster holding?

Who else is joining in?

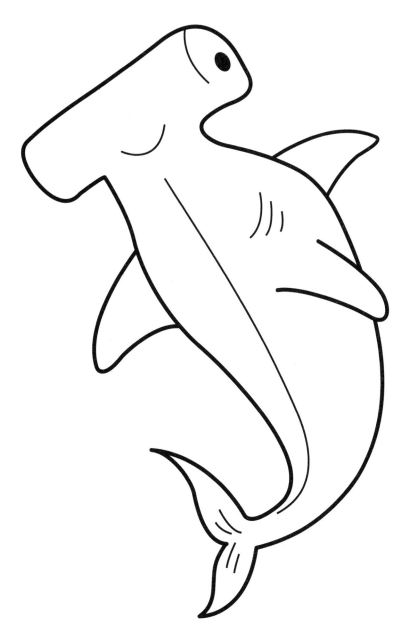

Who is hiding under
the Hammerhead shark?

Where does the hermit crab live?

Can you help decorate
the hermit crab's shell?

Sting ray tower!
How many more can fit on?

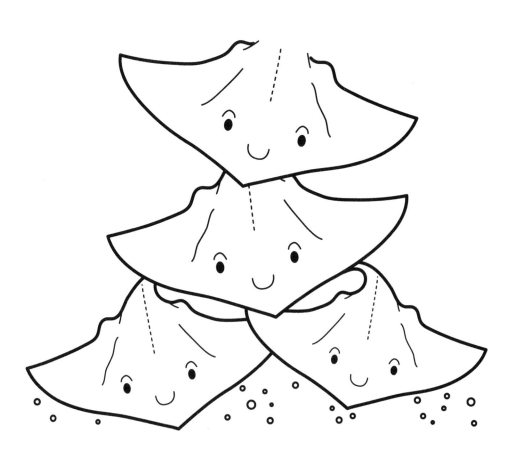

What does a sting ray's tail look like?

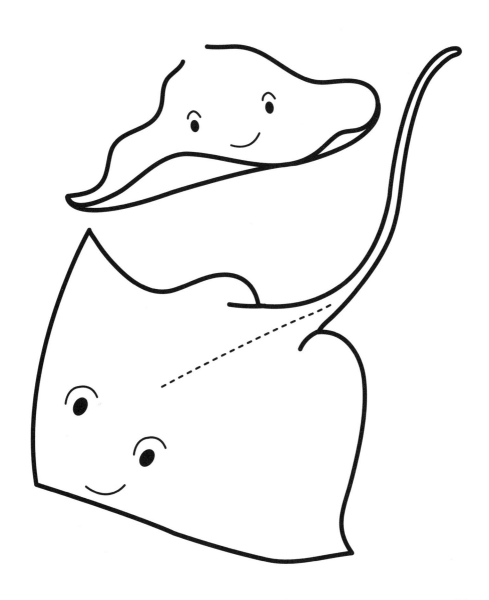

The swordfish is a really fast swimmer,
helped by its long bill.
What does it look like?

The swordfish are having a race.
Who crosses the finish line first?

The mommy seahorse needs to
find a home for her babies.
Can you draw one for her?

What does a seahorse's fin look like?

Crabs like to live in rock pools. What would you find there?

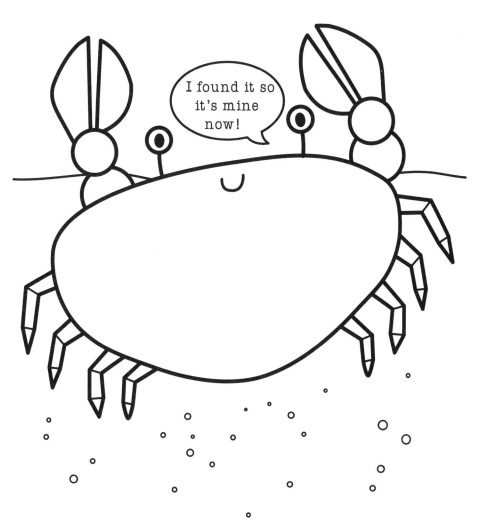

What is the crab holding in its claws?

The sea urchin rests on the sea bed.
Can you draw some coral around it?

What are the sea urchins sitting on?

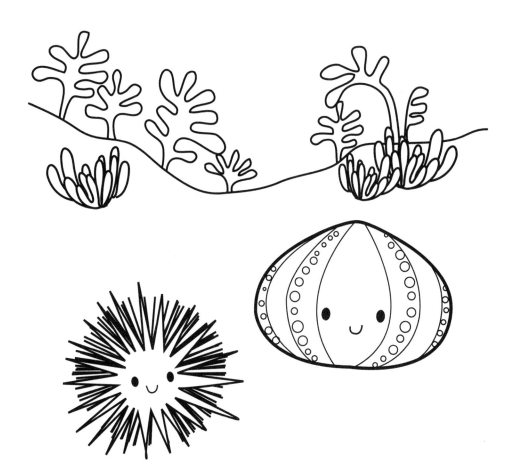

Sea anemones have lots of tentacles. Can you draw some for this one?

Who likes to play with the sea anemone?

Eels are really long.
Can you give this one a tail?

Eels like to swim through the plants
at the bottom of the sea.
Can you draw some more?

What does a sea otter's face look like?

The sea otter likes to keep cool
when it's a hot day.
What is in the sky above him?

What is the sea lion looking at?

Can you draw a design on the sea lion's ball?

These jellyfish have gotten
all tangled up!
Can you draw their tentacles?

What is missing from this jellyfish?

Where are the shrimp marching to?

Where does this fish live?

What do these fish need
to help them swim?

What patterns would look nice on these angel fish?

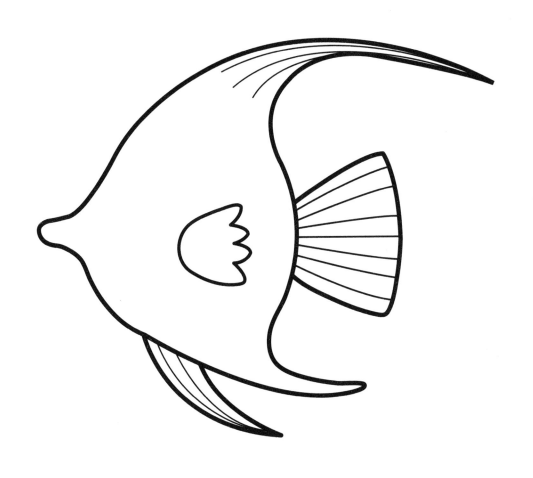

Can you draw a face for this fish?

Where does this fish like to play?

What different spiky fish can you draw?

What is the goldfish looking at?

What do these goldfish like to eat?

A group of fish is called a school.
Can you give these fish different colors?

Who is the fish hiding from?

What is the squid holding
in her tentacles?

How many tentacles can you give the squid?

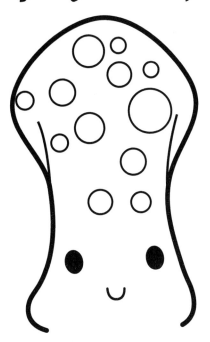

Who likes to swim in the coral reef?

Can you draw some more coral on the sea bed?

The manatee has spotted a friend hiding
in the cave. Who can it be?

What is missing from this manatee?

There are lots of creatures living
in the sea.
Who else would you find there?

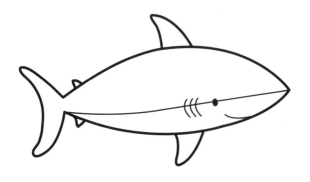

Who lives in these shells?